KU-007-028

Flight of Fear

Janice Pimm ● Jon Stuart

Contents

Welcome to Micro World! ..... page 2
The Zapper-BITE ..... page 5
Air Attack ..... page 13

OXFORD
UNIVERSITY PRESS

Macro Marvel
(billionaire inventor)

Welcome to Micro World.

Macro Marvel invented Micro World – a micro-sized theme park where you have to shrink to get in.

A computer called **CODE** controls Micro World and all the robots inside – MITEs and BITEs.

A MITE

A BITE

Disaster strikes!

CODE goes wrong on opening day.
CODE wants to shrink the world.

Macro Marvel is trapped inside the park …

Enter Team X!

Four micro agents – **Max, Cat, Ant** and **Tiger** – are sent to rescue **Macro Marvel** and defeat CODE.

Mini Marvel joins Team X.

Mini Marvel
(Macro's daughter)

In the last book ...

* Team X landed on the hot red planet.
* Tiger and Mini shrank and a MITE carried them to the Tower of Glass.
* It was a trap!

**CODE key
(1 collected)**

You are in the Galactic Orbit zone.

3

Before you read

Sound checker
Say the sounds.

**air   ear
ure**

Sound spotter
Blend the sounds.

l	ure

h	air

h	ear

b	ear	d

Tricky word
all

Into the zone
Can you remember where
Tiger and Mini are trapped?

4

The Zapper-BITE

The BITE sent a MITE to lure Tiger and Mini to the tower.

Hee hee!

Then the BITE shut the pair
of them in the tower.

Mini had her Gizmo.
It had all the facts.

Zapper-BITE

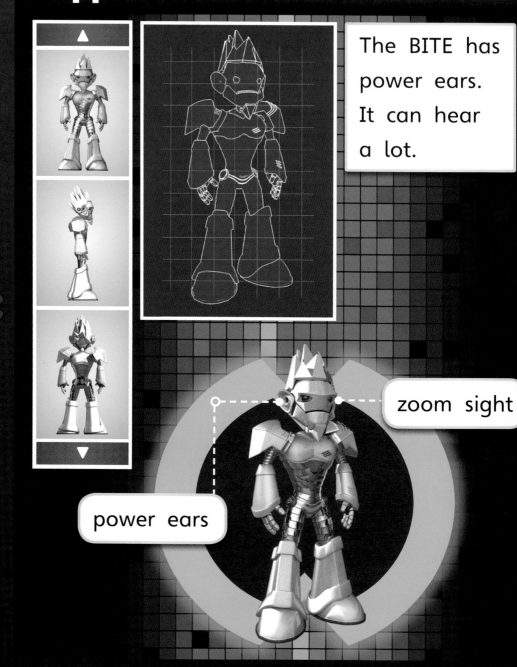

The BITE has power ears. It can hear a lot.

zoom sight

power ears

Attack!

Speed

Strength

Combat

Fright

red hair

black teeth

zap!

red beard

In Attack the BITE shoots lights.

Stop the BITE!

The CODE key is under its ear.

Get the CODE key to stop the BITE.

low you have read ...
The Zapper-BITE

ext checker

ook back at the story.
an you describe the BITE?

MITE fun

xplain how the BITE trapped
iger and Mini.

What shall I do with
Tiger and Mini?

Before you read

Sound checker
Say the sounds.

air   ear

ure

Sound spotter
Blend the sounds.

| f | ear |

| p | air |

| n | ear |

| m | a | n | ure |

Tricky words

they

all

Into the zone

How do you think Tiger and Mini might escape from the tower?

12

Air Attack

Tiger and Mini must get near the BITE to get the CODE key. The door is stuck.

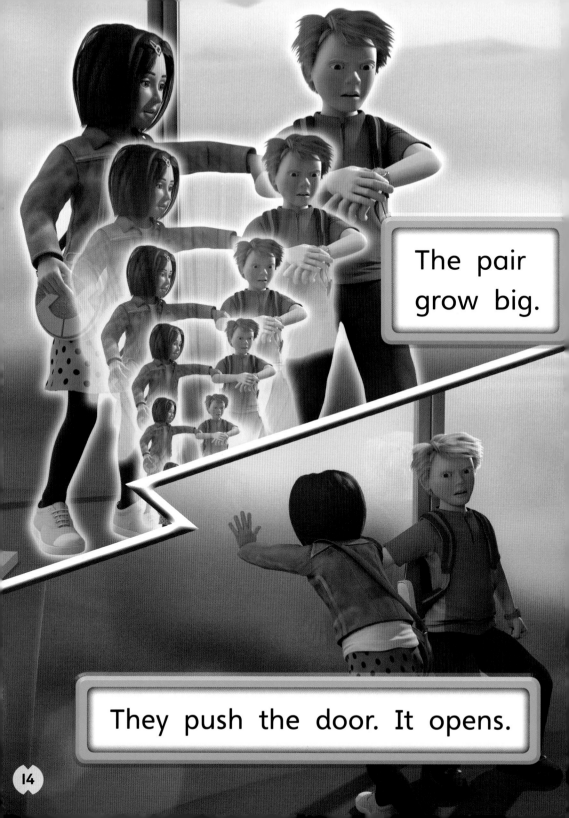

The pair grow big.

They push the door. It opens.

The BITE hears them.
Tiger and Mini run.

The BITE attacks.
Mini lures it into the garden.

It slips in the manure.

The BITE is soon in the air.
It shoots lights at Tiger and Mini.

Tiger puts his bounce boots on.
The pair run away.

Quick!

Wait!

Is that Cat in her jet pack?
She has no fear.

Cat gets near the BITE.
She pulls out the CODE key.
The BITE shuts down.

Cat zooms back to the rocket.
Tiger and Mini go too.

They all go to the exit.
Cat puts in the CODE key.
The door opens!

Now you have read ...
Air Attack

To get to the next zone we have to read the CODE words. Then the exit door will open. Can you help us read them?

norgoat	owzure
surth	gurthar
owck	zoiler
yoot	zoon
airzz	eard